# THE DREIDEL

## JUMBO COLORING AND ACTIVITY BOOK

# What is Hanukkah?

The history of Hanukkah, the Festival of Lights, comes from an ancient text. Over 2,000 years ago, a king named Antiochus IV Epiphanes invaded the land of Judea. He wanted all of the people living there to convert to his religion. He made laws that meant the Jewish people could not practice their religion anymore. He took over their holy Temple and dedicated it to the Greek god Zeus. Led by a family called the Maccabees, the Jewish people decided to fight back. It took years, but they finally defeated the army of Antiochus IV. They cleansed their Temple, installed a new altar, and rededicated it. According to Jewish teachings, there was only one small jar of holy oil left in the Temple that had not been ruined by Antiochus. It only had enough oil to light the Temple for one day, but it burned for eight days and nights until new sacred oil could be found. Today, families all over the world celebrate the rededication of the Temple and the miracles of Hanukkah with a joyous festival lasting eight days.

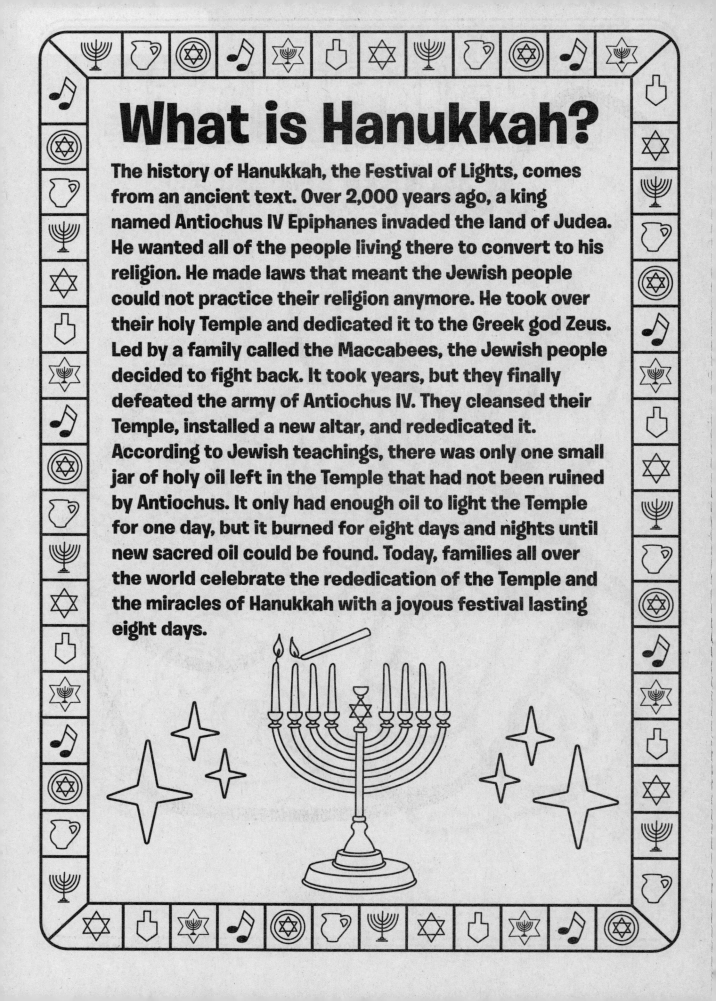

**Let's spin the dreidel!**

# Let's Count!

## How many dreidels do you count?

**Your Answer:**

# Words of Wisdom

How many words can you make using the letters in

## MIRACLE?

_____          _____

_____          _____

_____          _____

_____          _____

_____          _____

_____          _____

_____          _____

_____          _____

_____

# Matching

Draw lines connecting the matching objects.

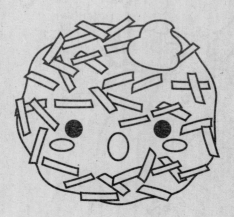
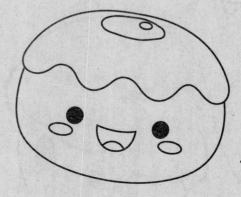

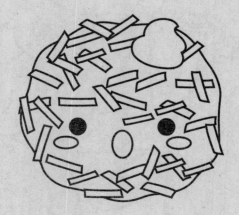
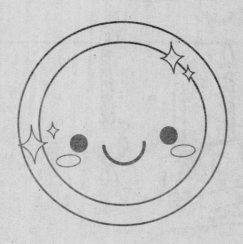

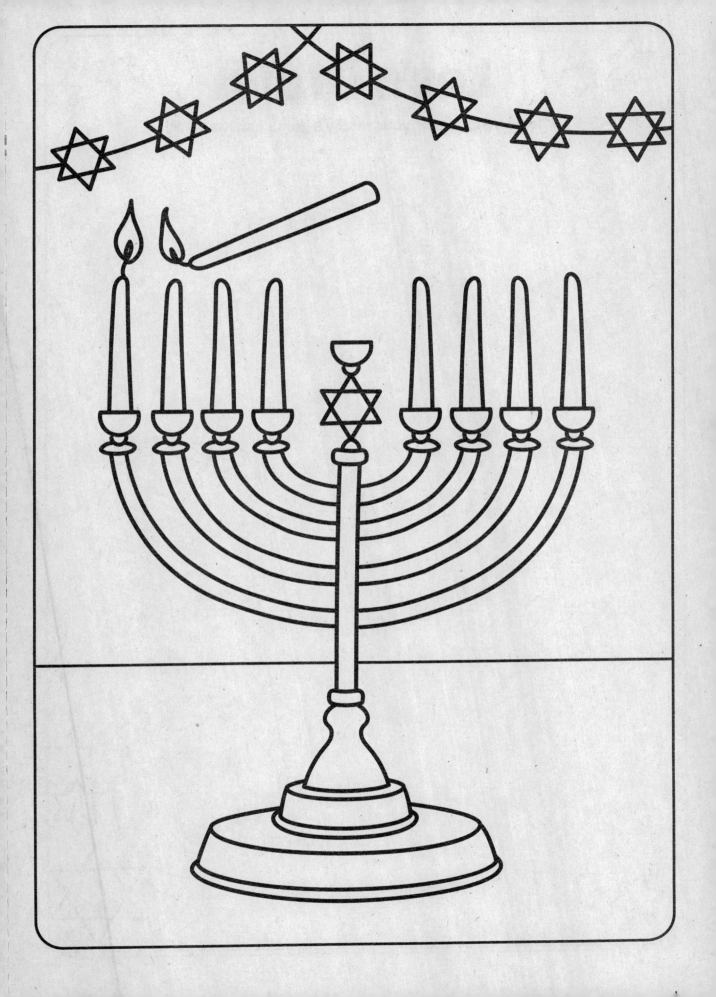

# Let's Draw!

**Draw a picture of your family's Hanukkah menorah.**

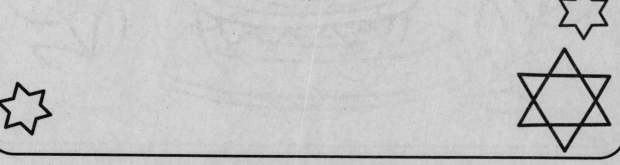

# Crack the Code

Use the code key to fill in the blanks and decipher the secret message.

= A    = C    = E    = F    = H

= I    = K    = L    = M    = N

# = O    = P    = R    = S    = T

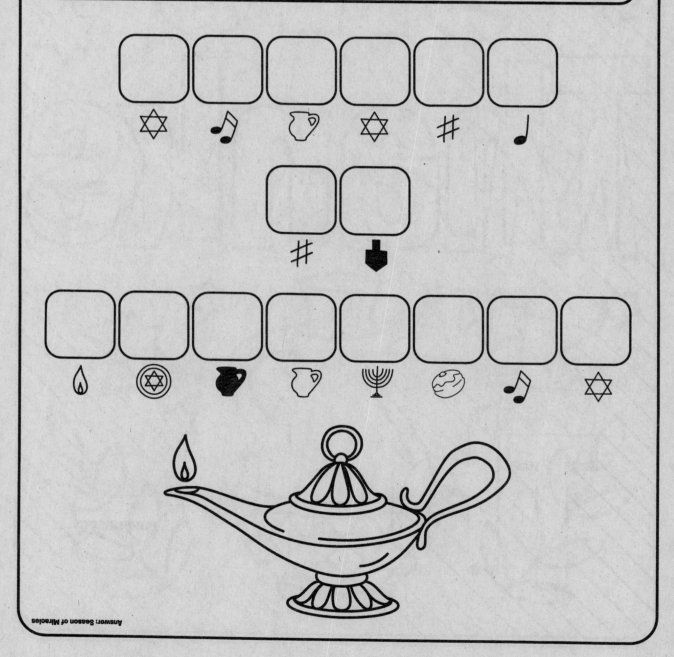

# Let's Draw!

**Use the grid as a guide to draw the dreidel in the space below.**

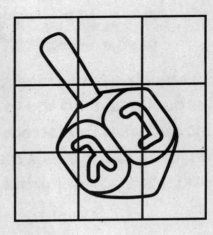

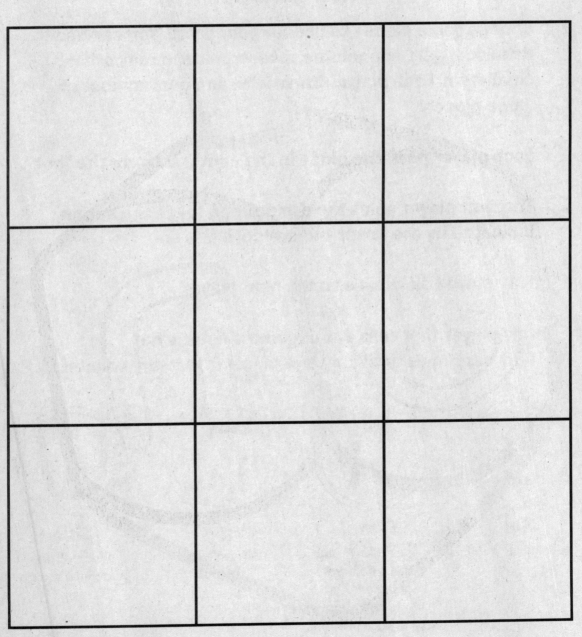

# Let's Play Dreidel!

A dreidel is a four-sided spinning top, usually made of wood or plastic. On each of the four sides is a Hebrew letter–*nun*, *gimel*, *hey*, and *shin*. The letters form an acronym of the Hebrew phrase *Nes gadol hayah sham*, meaning "a great miracle happened there". Dreidel is a popular game that is traditionally played at Hanukkah.

## How to Play:

☆ Choose game pieces to use for your game. You can use Hanukkah gelt, chocolates, sweets, nuts, or any other small item. Each player starts with an equal number of game pieces.

☆ Each player puts one piece in the center to form the "pot".

☆ The first player spins the dreidel, and takes the action indicated by the letter the dreidel lands on.

☆ Play moves clockwise to the next player.

☆ Any player that runs out of game pieces is out. Play continues until only one player is left–the winner!

**Nun**

nothing; nothing

**Gimel**

everything; take the whole pot, each player puts one game piece in to start a new pot

**Hey**

half; take half the pot

**Shin**

give; put one piece into the pot

# Make Your Own Paper Dreidel

**Nun**
*nothing*

**Gimel**
*everything*

**Hey**
*half*

**Shin**
*give*

fold in

fold in

fold in

fold in

fold in

fold in

fold in

fold in

## Directions

1. Carefully cut along the black outer line.

2. Fold along the gray dotted lines.

3. Tape the fold in tabs to the inside to form the shape of your dreidel.

4. Push a pencil or straw through the top circle, all the way to the bottom.

5. Spin to win!

# Tic-Tac-Toe

**Challenge your family and friends!**

# Find It Fast!

**Most menorahs have seven arms, but the Hanukkah menorah has nine.
Can you spot the Hanukkah menorah?**

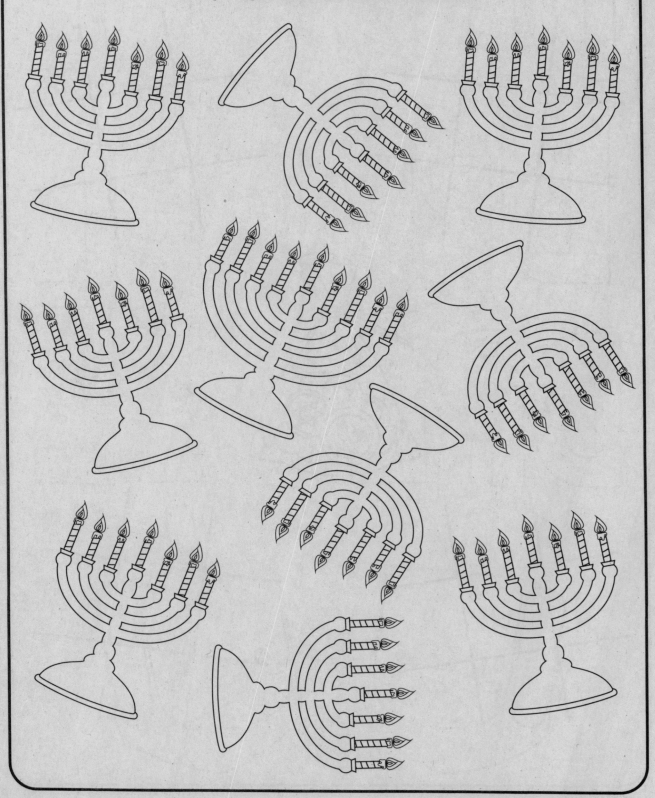

# DREIDEL
# Dreidel
# DREIDEL

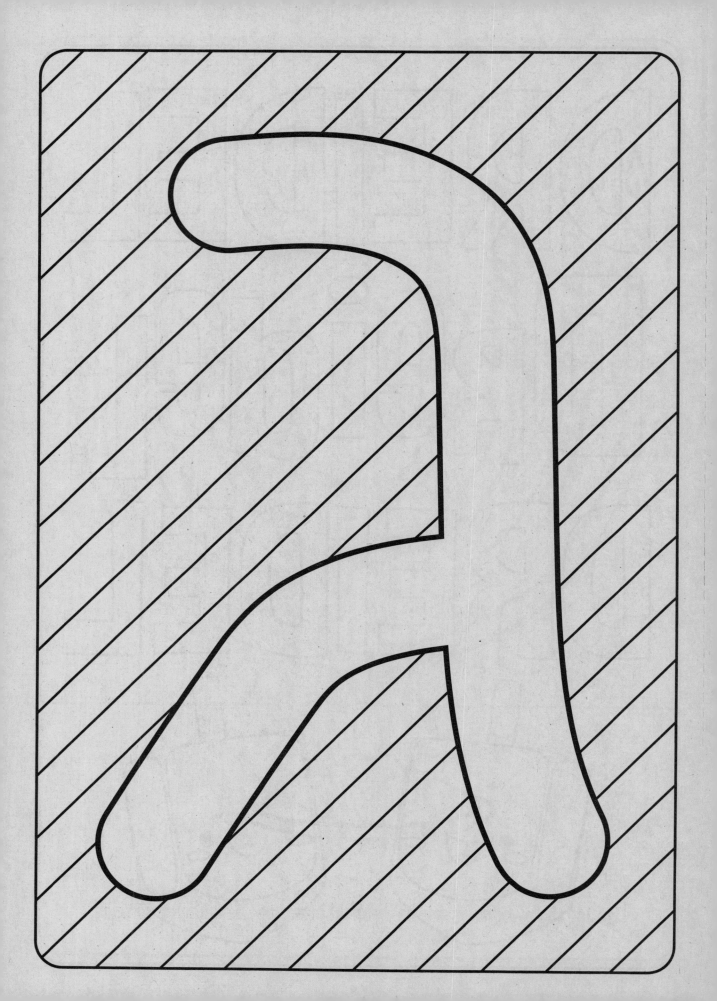

**Lighting the menorah is one of the most important Hanukkah traditions.**

I love to hear the story of Hanukkah!

# Rhyme Time!

### How many words can you think of that rhyme with

# PEACE?

_____     _____

_____     _____

_____     _____

_____     _____

_____     _____

_____     _____

_____

_____

_____

# Words of Wisdom

How many words can you make using the letters in

# FESTIVAL OF LIGHTS?

_____    _____

_____    _____

_____    _____

_____    _____

_____    _____

_____    _____

_____

_____

_____

# Printing Practice

**Color the picture and practice printing the word.**

DREIDEL

# Squares

**example**

Challenge a friend to a game and take turns drawing a line from one dot to another. If you make a line that completes a square, put your initial inside that box. The player with the most squares at the end of the game wins!

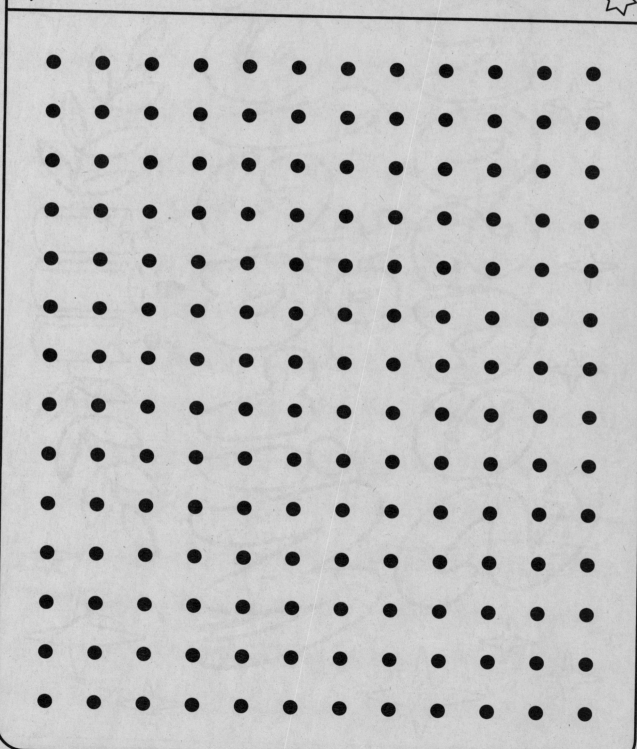

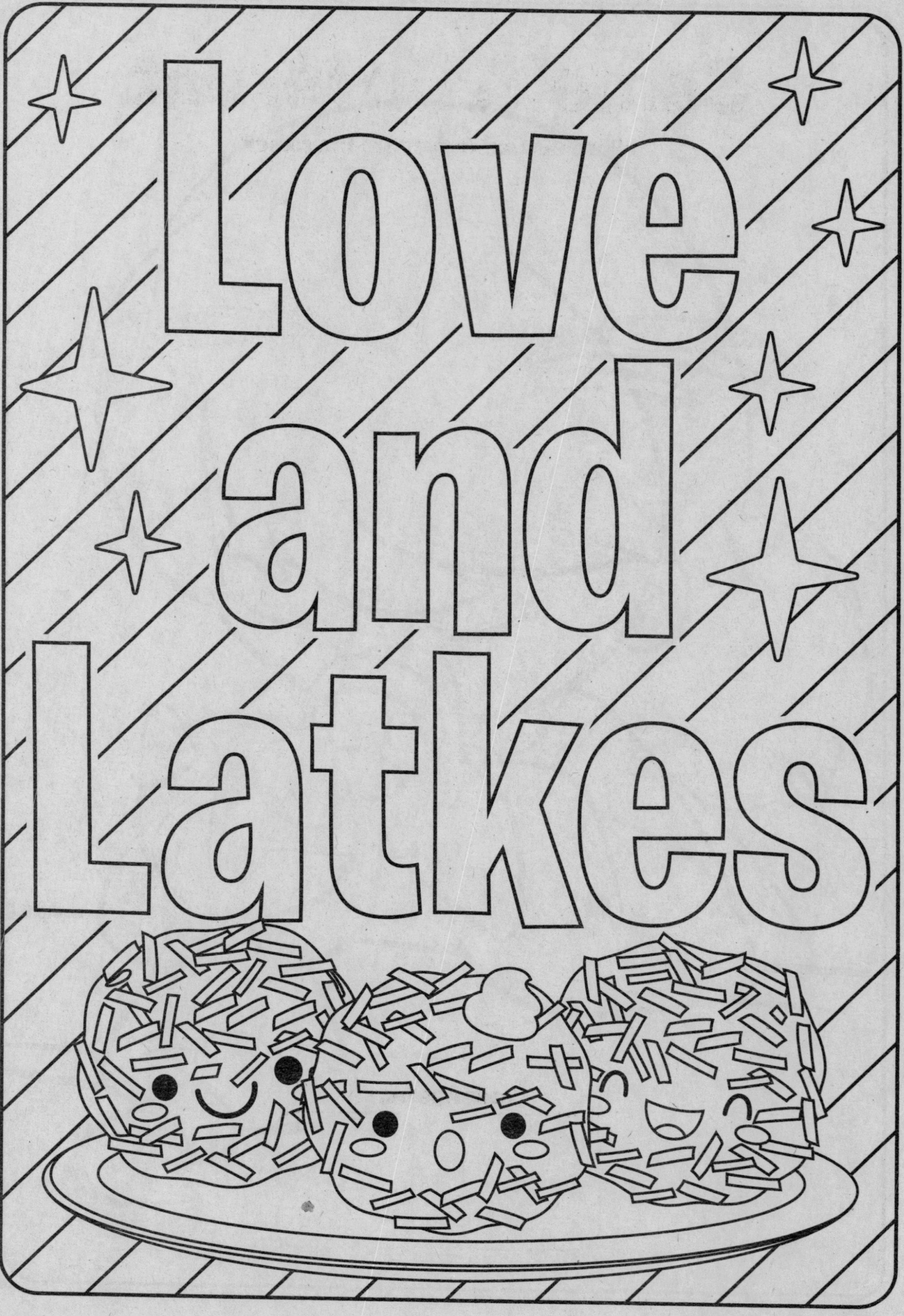
Love
and
Latkes

# Same & Different

**Which two *sufganiyot* are the same?**

A

B

C

D

## Your Answers:

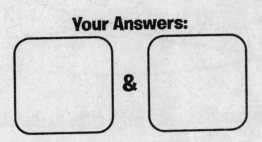

&

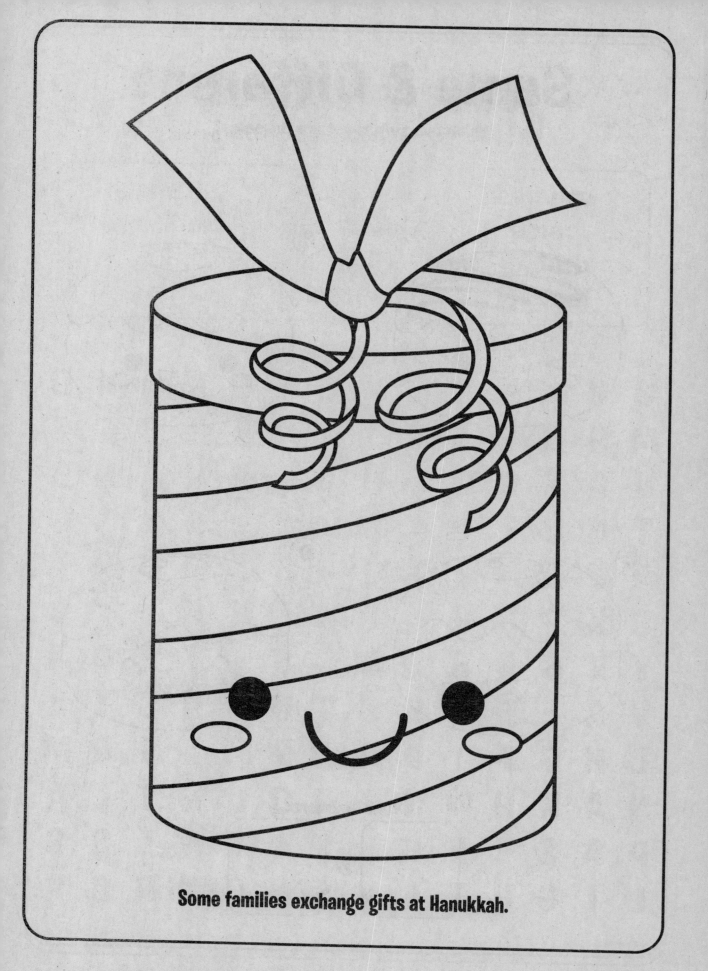

**Some families exchange gifts at Hanukkah.**

# Word Search

**Find and circle the Hanukkah words in the puzzle.**

| candles | Hanukkah | shamash |
|---------|----------|---------|
| coins | latkes | traditions |
| dreidel | light | |
| festival | menorah | |

```
G R M K H N M E N O R A H O
M H B Y T C G Z V B K C S K
J A F C P L H E C R H A N B
T N V T R A D I T I O N S G
R U A M K T J R D E R D P T
S K P D R K L B E A P L Y S
Y K C G S E N C S I Y E D H
V A E O P S Q T P G D S T A
L H G F I D R W R M L E R M
N A K H W N T R Q D N T L A
P A S E F E S T I V A L S S
L I G H T F Y S N C M R D H
```

# Let's Draw!

Use the grid as a guide to draw
the candle in the space below.

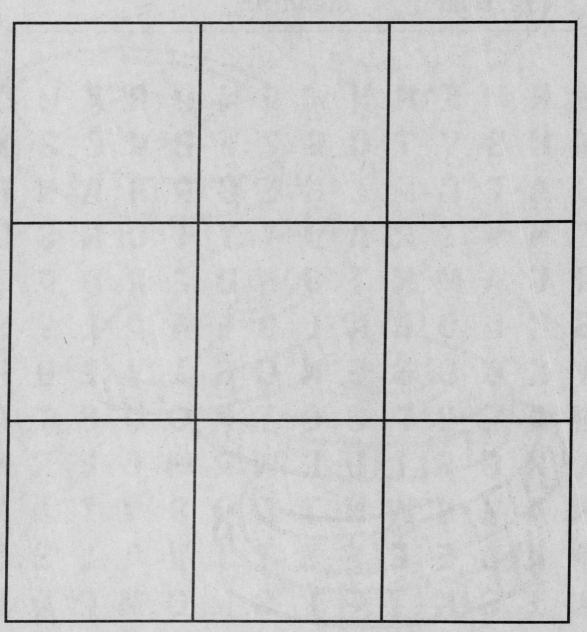

# Word Scramble

Unscramble the letters to correctly spell the Hanukkah words.

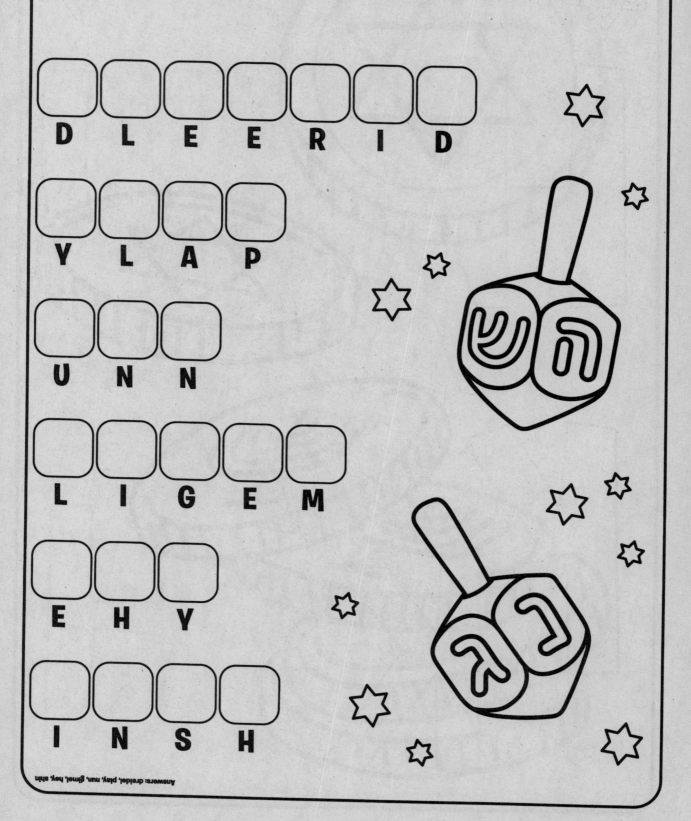

D L E E R I D

Y L A P

U N N

L I G E M

E H Y

I N S H

# Printing Practice

**Color the picture and practice printing the word.**

HANUKKAH

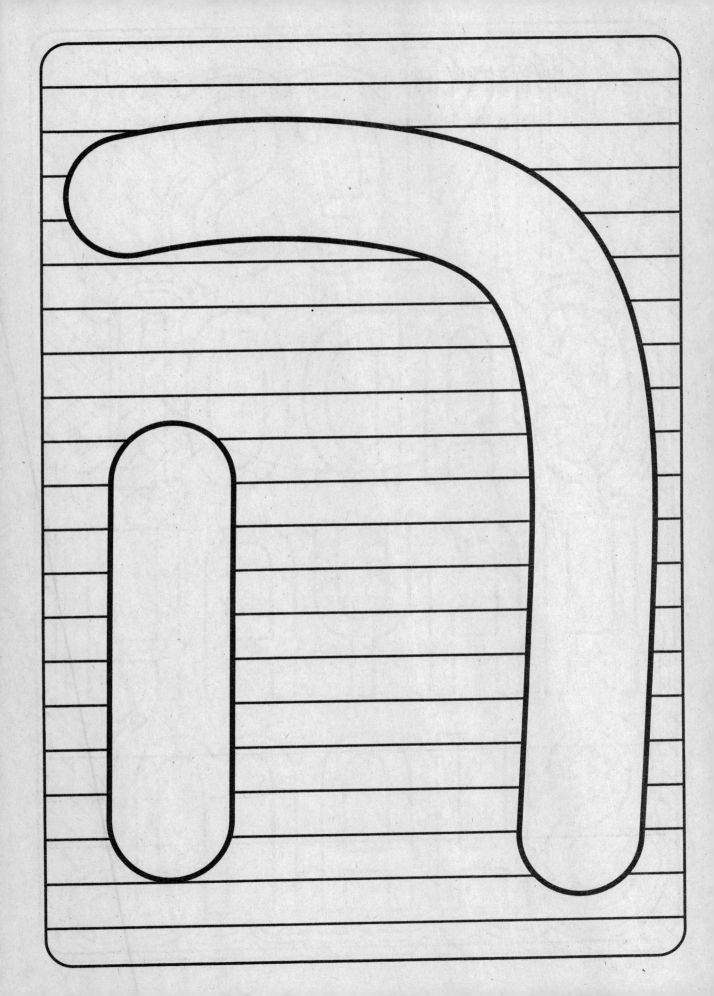

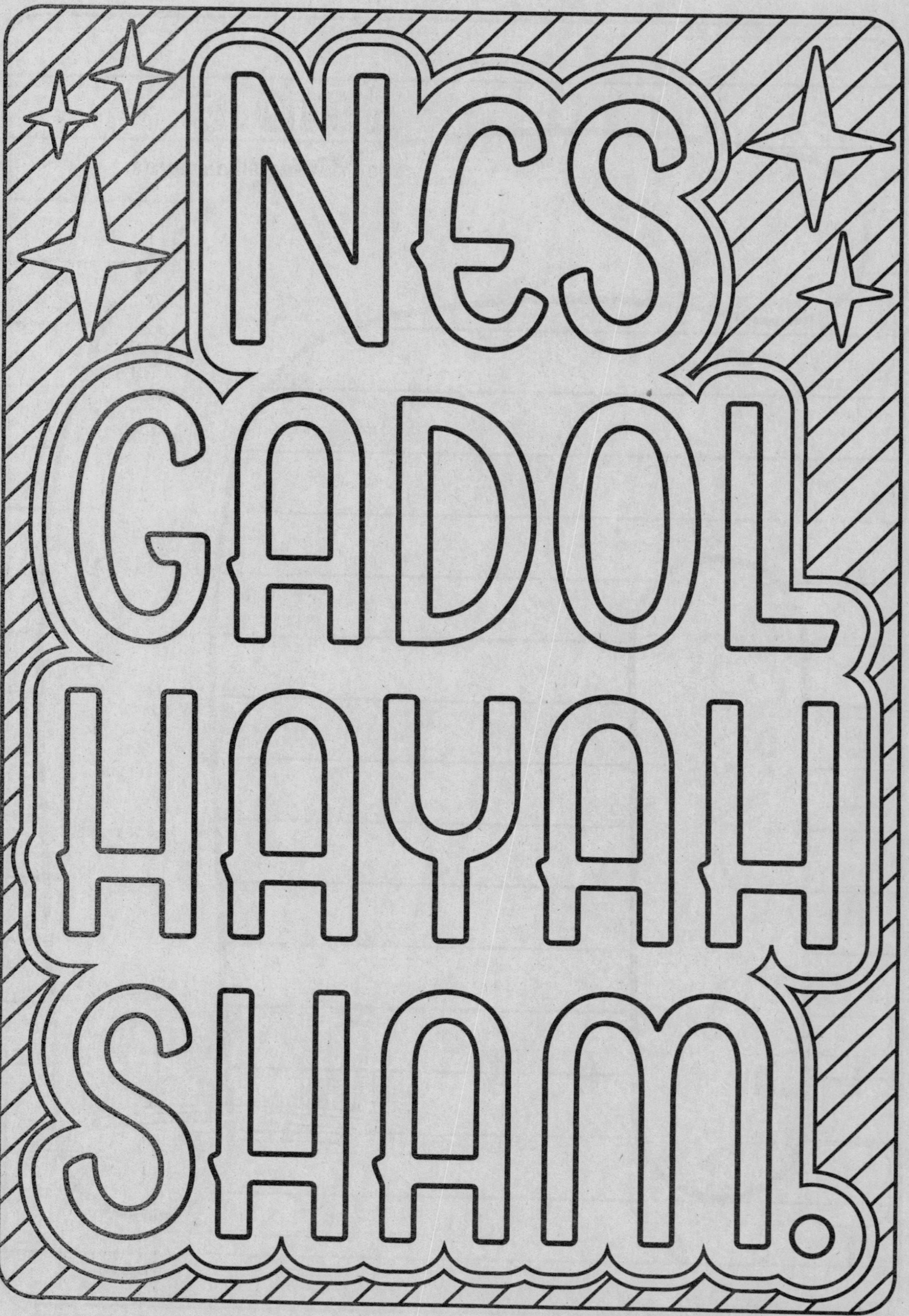
NES
GADOL
HAYAH
SHAM!

# Word Scramble

Unscramble the letters to correctly spell the Hanukkah words.

L P E M E T

A B A M E C S E C

C D I A N D T E I O

R I C A M E L

L A T R A

I L O

# Let's Count!

## How many latkes do you count?

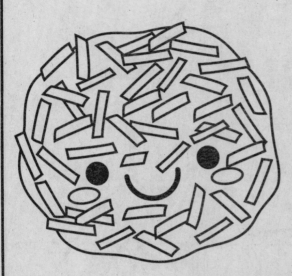
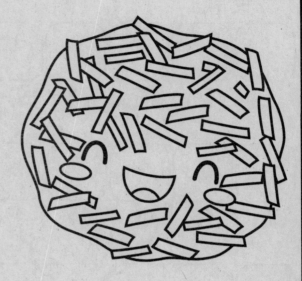

**Your Answer:**

# Matching

Draw lines connecting the matching objects.

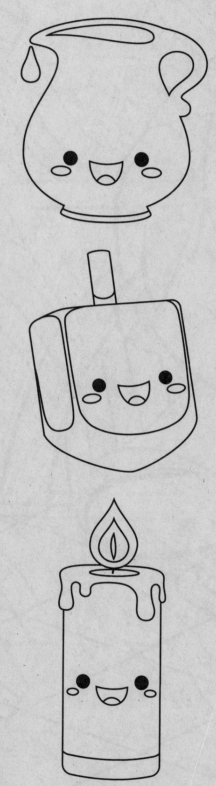

# Tic-Tac-Toe

## Challenge your family and friends!

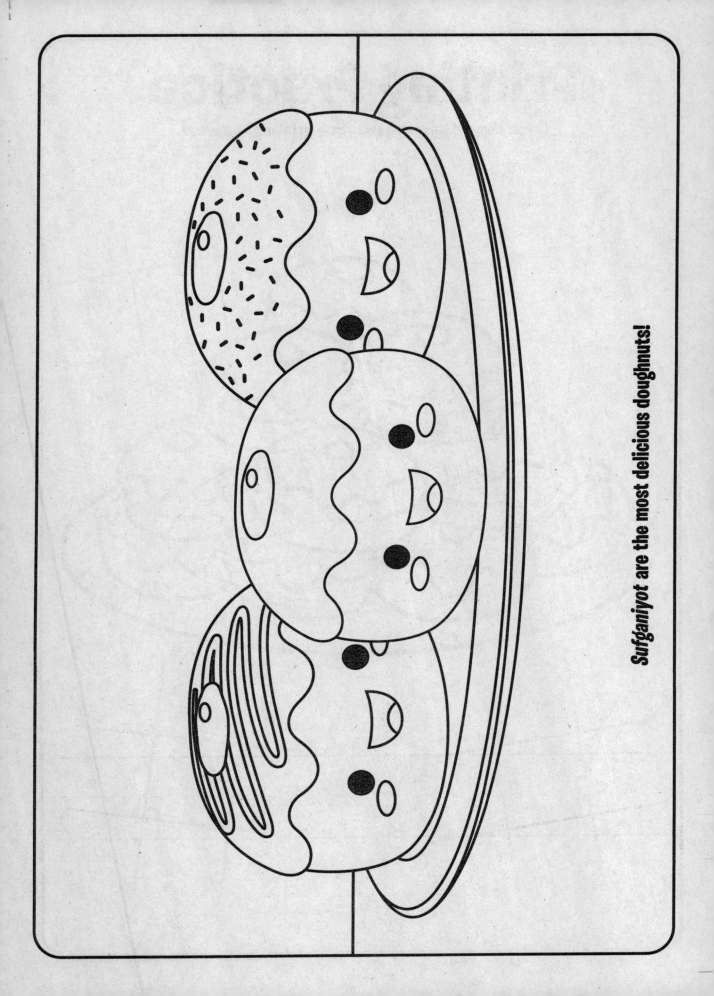

Surfganiyot are the most delicious doughnuts!

# Printing Practice

Color the picture and practice printing the word.

TRADITIONS

# Let's Draw!

**Use the grid as a guide to draw the gelt in the space below.**

**Many families give Hanukkah gelt to children.**

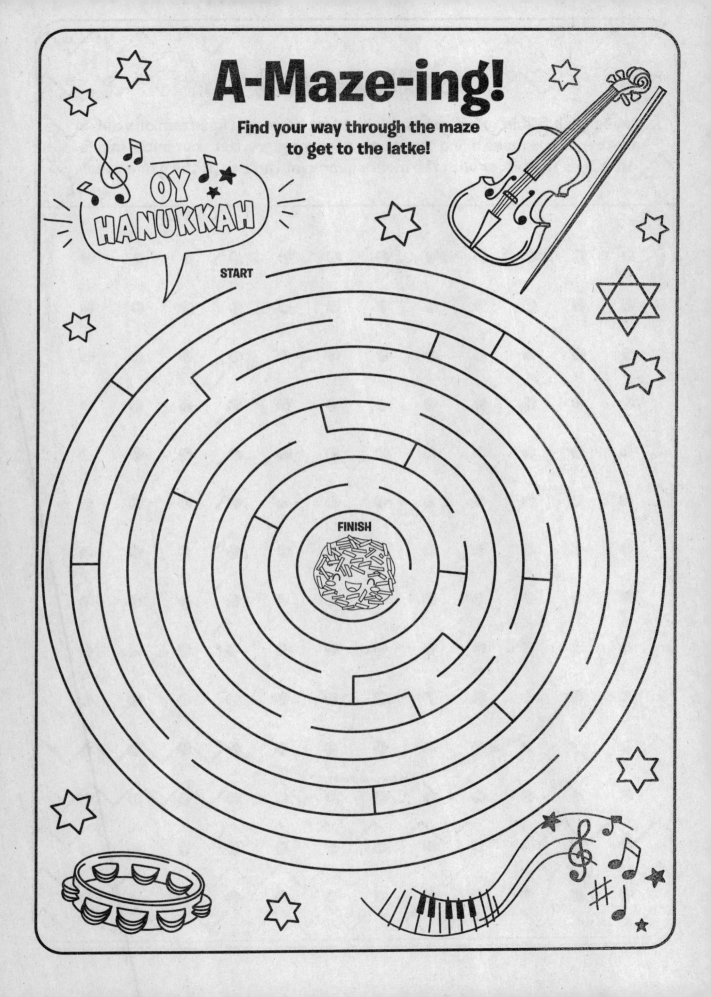

# Squares

Challenge a friend to a game and take turns drawing a line from one dot to another. If you make a line that completes a square, put your initial inside that box. The player with the most squares at the end of the game wins!

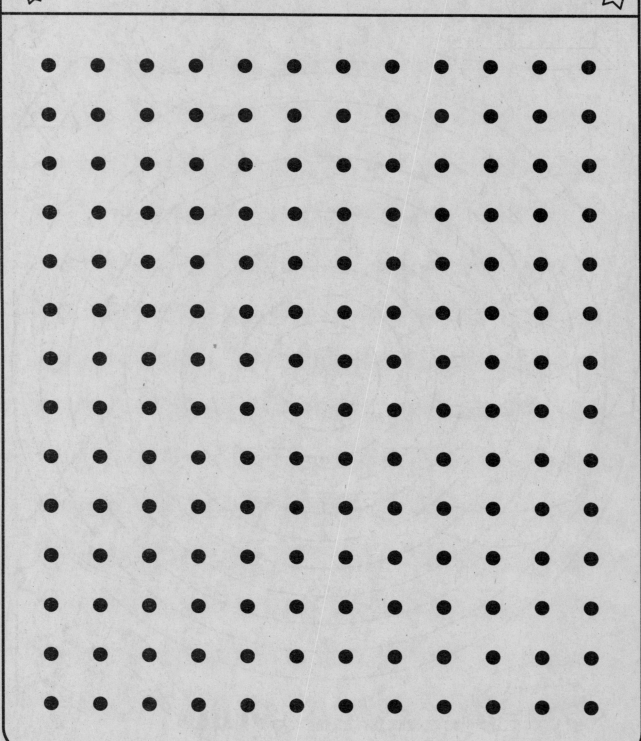

**We give thanks for the miracle of Hanukkah.**

# Get Creative!

**Instead of receiving gifts, many families give tzedakah at Hanukkah.
Tzedakah may be money, gifts, kindness, or service given to those in need.
Write about a way you could give tzedakah.**

_____

_____

_____

_____

_____

_____

_____

_____

_____

_____

# Sudoku

Can you complete these Hanukkah sudoku puzzles?
Each image should appear only once in each row and each column.

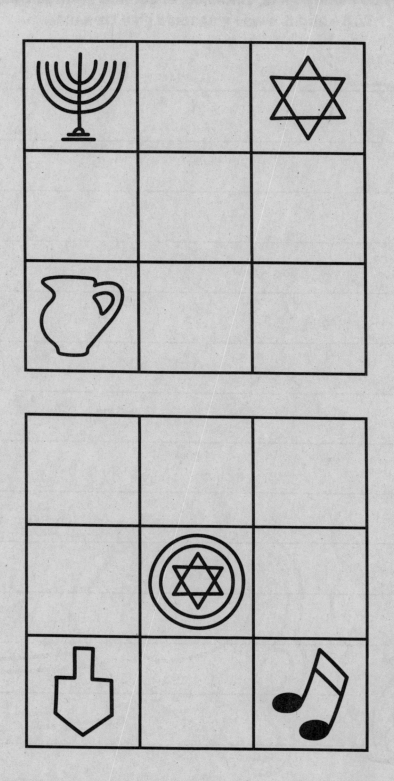

# Menorah Math

For the first night of Hanukkah, you'll need a shamash and one candle to light your Hanukkah menorah. On the second night, you'll need a shamash and two candles. How many candles will you need to celebrate all eight nights of Hanukkah?

**Night 1** 🕯 + 🕯 = ☐

**Night 2** 🕯 + 🕯 + 🕯 = ☐

**Night 3** 🕯 + 🕯 + 🕯 + 🕯 = ☐

**Night 4** 🕯 + 🕯 + 🕯 + 🕯 + 🕯 = ☐

**Night 5** 🕯 + 🕯 + 🕯 + 🕯 + 🕯 + 🕯 = ☐

**Night 6** 🕯 + 🕯 + 🕯 + 🕯 + 🕯 + 🕯 + 🕯 = ☐

**Night 7** 🕯 + 🕯 + 🕯 + 🕯 + 🕯 + 🕯 + 🕯 + 🕯 = ☐

**Night 8** 🕯 + 🕯 + 🕯 + 🕯 + 🕯 + 🕯 + 🕯 + 🕯 + 🕯 = ☐

## Total number of candles = ☐

# Words to Know!

**_Chag same'ach_** - Hebrew for "happy holiday"

**dreidel** - a four-sided top marked with Hebrew letters and used to play a game, traditionally at Hanukkah

**gelt** - money, often given to children at Hanukkah wrapped in gold foil

**_gimel_** - the third letter of the Hebrew alphabet

**Hanukkah** - eight-night Jewish festival celebrating the rededication of the Temple

**_hey_** - the fifth letter of the Hebrew alphabet

**latkes** - fried potato pancakes, usually served at Hanukkah

**menorah** - a candelabra used in Jewish worship

**_nes gadol hayah sham_** - Hebrew for "a great miracle happened there"

**_nun_** - the fourteenth letter of the Hebrew alphabet

**shamash** - candle used to light the other candles on a menorah, also called the attendant or servant candle

**_shin_** - the twenty-first letter of the Hebrew alphabet

**_sufganiyot_** - fried jelly doughnut, usually served at Hanukkah

**tzedakah** - gifts of kindness, service, or charity, from the Hebrew word for righteousness